The **Oldie**

Loony Toons

Loony Toons

Chosen by
Richard Ingrams

Oldie Publications Ltd
London

This compilation first published by
Oldie Publications Ltd

Copyright © 1998 Oldie Publications Ltd

The publishers would like to thank the respective copyright owners
for permission to include illustrations in this volume

A CIP catalogue record for this book is available from the British Library

ISBN 1-901170-06-3

Printed by Woolnough Bookbinding Ltd
Cover Illustration by Ham Khan

Acknowledgement

The Oldie wishes to thank all the cartoonists whose work is reproduced in this volume, and all those who have submitted cartoons to the magazine over the years.

'I caught her running away to join the media circus'

'What is that perfume you're wearing?'

'For God's sake man - think of the pollution!'

'Ah Henry, the constable was so understanding about the television licence, I told him about the body under the garage'

'Goodness, is that the time? I must fly!'

'My poem is called; My Dad, The Asset Stripper'

'That's typical of this airline – our luggage has been washed up on a different island'

'We can't cure you, but we can try to get
you on Panorama if you like'

'OK – I'll hold'

DEIRDRE McGURKE
WILL BE SIGNING
COPIES OF HER BOOK
'COPING
WITH
PMT'
HERE AT NOON
TODAY!

'She's decided she won't turn up and says stuff the lot of you...'

'Sorry, the duck's off'

'It's too late to agree with me now – I've changed my mind'

'Dad, why are we called 'Travellers'?'

'Coming dear – I'm just putting the dragon out!'

'Viewers are warned that the following programme includes language strong enough to knock the bollocks off a shit shovel'

'I'm sorry Mr Hodges, the headmaster is insisting on a drugs test'

'Is this the road to ruin?'

'More E vicar?'

'You scratch my back, Perkins, and I'll stab yours'

'I like it'

'My husband eats like a bird – do you have any regurgitated insects?'

'But doesn't the council object to you opening on Sundays?'

'I'm still looking for Jude the Obscure'

'Remember, guys – no undesirables'

'Bang goes the 'Feel-Good' factor'

'It's telescoped to allow for pregnancies'

Archbishop of Cadbury

*'All I want is a room somewhere,
far away from the cold night air,
with one enormous chair...'*

'Start again, Ned. You were in tune'

*'My hamster died. Could you send
a stress counsellor round?'*

'Now, let's see, what would you both like?'

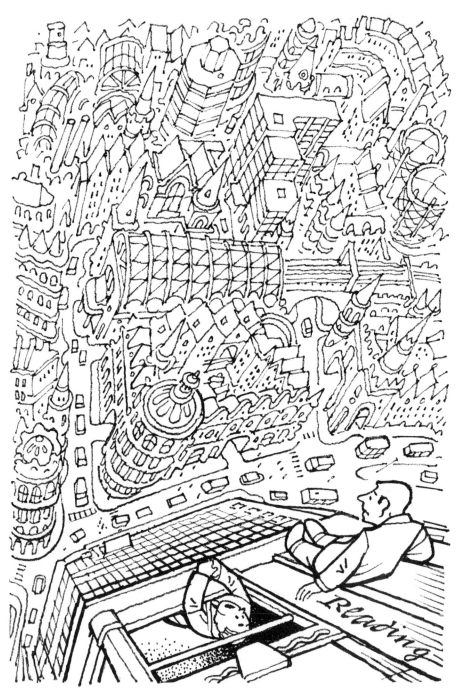

'But Arthur, you could land in a very unfashionable postal district'

'The other way Oscar, if you want to do the Genius gag'

'Sky has given us a far greater choice of programmes to switch off'

'I'm afraid it's merely a forgery of a forgery of one of master forger Han Van Meegeren's bogus Vermeers'

'Well, I say we sue for compensation'

'Five minutes everybody'

*'Sure he looks tough
but he can't hold his drink'*

'I know we shall all miss the services of a well loved handyman'

'Shall I be Mother Superior?'

'He smoked a hundred a day – so I put his ashes in the ashtray'

'Wouldn't it just be easier to see a doctor about your condition, Neville?'

'I think they're so much more authentic than plastic flowers'

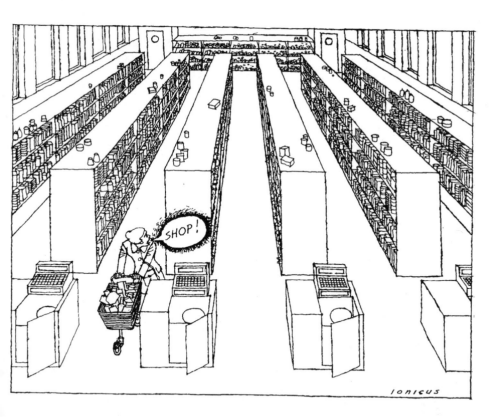

'Stop! Misunderstood victim of an uncaring society!'

'That's a pretty kettle of fish'

'Don't even think about comparing
me to a summer's day, you bastard'

'Where exactly do you get these
stabbing pains?'

'*"Who's been surfing* my *Internet?" said Father Bear...*'

'This episode calls for your resentful anger.
Oh, and I hear they'll not be renewing your contract'

'...and he's taking his money with him'

'Crown? No. I thought you had it'

'What I find interesting is the way that traditional styles are co-existing with the new'

'He's one of the best, our lad – untrustworthy, cruel, avaricious!'

'Stand back or I shout'

'This is the special episode of Eastenders – the one where somebody smiles'

'I believe they spliced one too many flounder genes into this tomato'

'Your co-directors wish you a speedy recovery by a vote of 3 to 2'

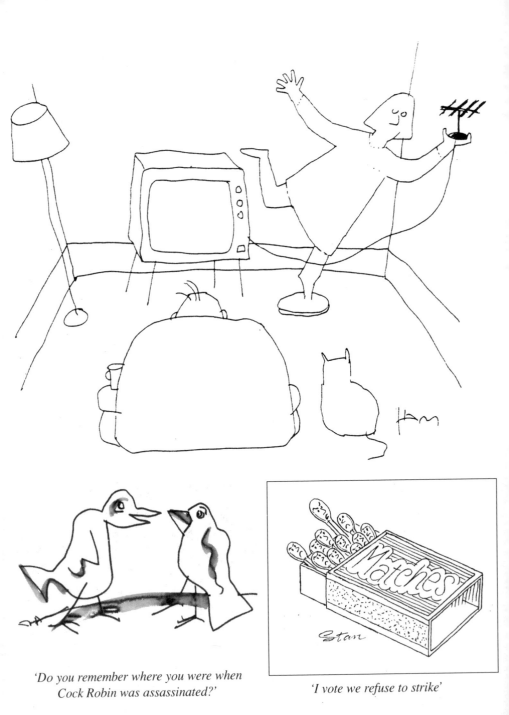

'Do you remember where you were when
Cock Robin was assassinated?'

'I vote we refuse to strike'

'The last time I was in here they taught me to read and write – now I'm in for forgery'

'Before we go, could you cut the hedge?'

*'Goodnight Nanook
Great housewarming party'*

'Mavis! Your bath is ready!'

'He must have escaped from one of those low-security prisons'

'It was the wife really – she just liked the name David'

'Smacking or non-smacking?'

'I hope you don't mind, we started without you'

'If I've told you once I've told you a
thousand times – don't exaggerate'

'I'm under stress, Miss Gibson. Come in and bite my nails'

'I'll have the five loaves and two fishes'

'They seem very strict with their children'

LIFTS TO FLATS

'Why don't you get the train to work like everybody else?'

cooper

'Anyone else want to question the morality of our business?'

'You will meet many tall, dark, strangers'

'Now my personal favourite: Market research shows a very positive response from the general public to this image'

'I hear he's filthy rich'

'I'm just nipping out to buy a loaf of bread, a packet of biscuits, a new coat and a tin of peaches'

'Have you seen my toupee anywhere?'

'Yes – I'd like to put out a fatwa on someone'

'Your majesty has a cold.
The type most frequently caught
by commoners!'

'One, please'

'He's going clubbing'

'Is anything up with Gerald? He seems a bit distant'

'Is there a way to adjust the escalator's speed?'

'We call it placebo surgery. It doesn't work but it's a lot cheaper'

'Thought of names yet?'

'It makes you look years younger, sir'

61

You can tell he's guilty – it's written all over his face'

'As to the charge of illegal entry, the accused would like
58, 943, 762 similar offences to be taken into account'

'Do you have any pigs' hearts?'

'Might I suggest something in 'maternity'?'

Geoff Waterhouse

'A snake with an apple, would you Adam and Eve it?'

'I'd like you to meet Jim, he's my right-hand man'

'You never plead with me to stay like you used to'

'Arrr, this be Blind Pooh, Cap'n'

'Eye of newt, wing of bat, hair of dog...'

*'Hurry up – I've only got time for
a soundbite'*

'Any chance of sitting about doing nothing?'

'Our prodigal son's returned
saying he's a vegetarian'

'That pose is perfect, m'lord'

'Could you just unblock the sink before exterminating anyone?'

'It's not so much a tête-á-tête as a tête-á-derriere'

'I take it you didn't get in, then'

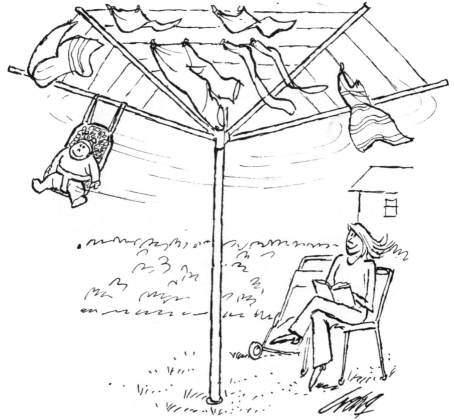

'...and to your right, you can't see anything either'

'I believe, Gentlemen, this may be an appropriate time to reveal the extent of our own research in medical science...'

'You are going on a long journey'

'Of course I take you seriously, you cheeky little love pumpkin'

'...and if we miss three payments on the TV and four payments on the lounge carpet we'll have enough for a downpayment on a new 3 piece suite'

'I've got satellite'

'...and now can we have one with the bride and the bridegroom's parents?'

'Albert takes his neighbourhood watch duties very seriously'

'It's all state-of-the-art, except him'

*'Perhaps we should rob the rich, but then lend to the poor at a
reasonable rate of interest?'*

'One for the road rage?'

'A pint of lager – and put it in a straight glass...'

'We can have it vandalised for you at no extra cost'

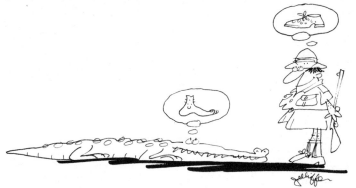

'...and when you awake you'll believe my
fees to be extremely reasonable'

'We were looking for a person with
'get up and go'. Now we want you to
get up and go!'

'Accept a transfer charge call?
What does he look like?'

'Oh, and just one other thing, Henderson – if you win you're fired'

'No, I don't want a bag or cashback and I haven't got a car park voucher or a loyalty card. I just want to pay for the newspaper and get on with my life'

'I see Ingersoll's still testing drugs on himself'

'I wish you wouldn't bring your work home with you'

'We're so lucky being paid to do something we enjoy'

'I sometimes wish you had another career!'

'I'm the token cretin to make the others look like intellectuals'

*'I won't spoil your weekend, Higgins – come and see me
first thing Monday morning'*

'Jeremy, why can't we talk instead of you bottling things up all the time?'

'I didn't realise you had step-children, Henry'

'Can you go to the loo or something – I'd like to make an entrance'

'The menu? That will be £5 sir'

'Right from the start of the holiday we didn't get on, Cilla'

'Reclaim your Inner-child in your own time, Pringle'

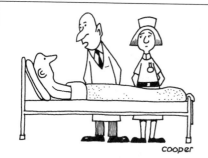

'Well Mr Jones, as you didn't die, we now have a small problem of bed shortage...'

'Would you mind accompanying me to the police station, sir – only this is a very rough area'

'He had his first hangover today'

'Where's Rolf?'

'As you can see, we have a Neighbour from Hell'

'This job comes with a real challenge – like trying to live on the salary we pay'

*'When did you opt for a
downshift in lifestyle?'*

'Do you think we ought to tell them?'

'You did? At your age?'

'Don't panic – he always feigns death
when it's his round'

'First let them try their hand at pronouncing it – THEN tell them it's off'

'Looks like they're kicking Hadley upstairs'

de la Nougerede

'I hate the mad rush to the seaside'

'So let me just run this one by you,
My Lord...'

'Can you hang on until I move
my BMW, Wilsher?'

'Well I'm going to bloody assertiveness
training whether you think I need it or not'

AIRPORT

FAT
BLOKE
WITH
STICKY
OUT
EARS

'Postcode?'

'So, you're the new accountant'

'I said to myself "Now he looks interest-ing" the moment you crawled through the door'

'Take no notice, Susan, he's at that inquisitive age'

'He's very proud of his
humble beginnings'

'Don't worry, I've been married for 35
years so I'm used to turbulence'

'Righto, Doris, if anybody cuts us up, let
the bastards have it'

'I'm not sure if I told you this, Oliver,
but warts and all will be extra'

'It's your Dad, alright – I can tell by his silly grin'

*'I don't think it's a serious
suicide attempt'*

'Bloody squatters!'